THE LEAN

PRIMER

Plant Edition

The Running Lean™ books are available at quantity discounts. For more information contact MCS Media, Inc. at 734-475-4301.

Address all other inquires to:

MCS Media, Inc.
888 Ridge Road
Chelsea, MI 48118
Telephone: 734-475-4301
Email: info@theleanstore.com

Cover concept and art design by Jody Williams
Content development by Roger Kremer and Tom Fabrizio

Printed in the United States of America

ISBN Number 0-9725728-5-6

The Lean Primer

Table of Contents

A Message from the
Publisher

There are hundreds if not thousands of books and references on Lean manufacturing. Almost too many to decide which one to use and which one not to use. *The Lean Primer* is the first workbook to present many of these tools and concepts where a basic, foundational understanding can occur. And from that basic understanding, Lean programs will emerge like never before.

The National Association of Job Shops and Small Manufacturers(NAJS) is a group of Lean practitioners from industry, training, consulting, and workforce development boards. NAJS is committed to teach, support, and share Lean manufacturing practices that relate specifically to the unique needs of job shops and small manufacturers.

No matter the size of the organization, from the prototype job shop of 3 persons to the larger Fortune 500 companies with thousands of employees at one location - and every type of manufacturing industry between - all have one thing in common; they must continually communicate effectively and efficiently to employees, whatever the subject may be. *The Lean Primer* was created to be the communication platform for all levels of the organization to gain the basic knowledge required to accept and contribute to Lean initiatives.

National Association of
NAJS
Job Shops and Small Manufacturers

The Lean Primer allows for a brief description of the Lean tools, followed by many practical applications of those tools. It provides the relevant information that should be used to teach an organization what Lean is and why go Lean.

The Lean Primer and the other workbooks in the *Running Lean™* series were created for use in job shops and small manufacturers. Each book was designed in a format that allows for immediate application of each of the tools.

In conclusion, it is an honor to have this book endorsed by the National Association of Job Shops and Small Manufacturers (NAJS).

Don Tapping
Publisher, MCS Media, Inc.
info@theleanstore.com

Reading Strategies

Sometimes reading a book from the first word to the last is not the most effective learning method. The steps listed below can make your reading easier, more enjoyable, and more effective.

Step 1: Get the big picture of the book by using the following list:

- Scan the table of contents to see how *The Lean Primer* is arranged.
- Flip through various pages to get a feel for the style, format, layout, design, and readability.
- Note the sample forms and worksheets that accompany each chapter.
- Glance at the graphics, icons, and margin notes.
- Read the first sentence of each chapter.

Step 2: Get involved in the Stages (Chapters) by following what is listed below:

- Scan the pages, noticing layout, bold headings, and key points in the text.
- Read the Section Overview.
- Read the overview text for the each Lean Action.
- Review key terms and other margin notes.
- Review the Reality Check information.
- Find the Personal Notes page and review it.
- Find the Summary Page.
- Review the Call to Action sample form at the end of the section.

Book Layout

Remember, each Lean Action is created from proven practices and provides significant tips and tools for immediate application. When you read the chapter summary, if there is something that you don't understand, review the material until you find the answer. Taking notes and using the Personal Notes pages will reinforce pertinent information. If working in a group, the notes will serve as a catalyst for group discussions and action planning.

You will notice that this book is laid out with several features to assist you in understanding the philosophies, concepts, and processes discussed.

Each section of the book is explained in the context of a recommended, realistic implementation plan. There are three main sections that correspond to the three phases of understanding Lean.

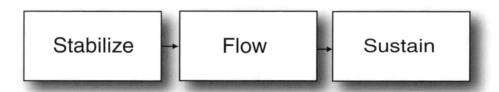

Each chapter includes a set of recommended Lean Actions to be implemented. Read through each Lean Action and use the Personal Notes pages to jot down thoughts and ideas specific to implementation. Remember, even though this book is about understanding the foundational concepts of Lean, there still must be some type of action resulting from reading this book.

Make notes about the current state of your organization related to the Lean Action being discussed at a very high level. Answer questions related to barriers and people to involve, and list any action items that come to mind. Once the Personal Notes pages are complete for the Lean Actions in a chapter, use them as a reference for the Call to Action form at the end of the chapter and begin planning your Actions to communicate these Lean tools and concepts.

Each concept and tool is explained with as little verbiage as possible, but with the maximum amount of functional content. The goal is to give enough detail to take action, with the suggested coures of action well-founded in fact and process control.

Section Overview provides a brief introduction to each of the Lean Actions in the section. Read the section overview to give you a big picture of the Lean concepts covered in the section.

Lean Actions provides information and tools to help you apply what you learn. Lean Actions are structured as follows:

- **Overview** provides a brief introduction and describes the purpose of the Lean Action.

- **Examples from the Floor** provides a look at a company's experiences related to the Lean Actions being discussed.

- **Reality Check "Ask Yourself"** gauges the current state of the organization and identifies action items. The Reality Check includes questions to ask yourself and step-by-step directions for implementing the Lean Action.

- **Personal Notes** provides space for making notes about how the Lean Action applies to your organization.

At the end of each chapter you will find summary materials and a Call to Action.

Chapter Summary summarizes the information outlined in the chapter including the key terms. If the summary and key terms are not clear, review the material in the book and seek additional resources before continuing to implement the Lean Actions.

Call to Action identifies steps based on the Lean Actions in the chapter and outlines a plan for immediate action. You will list action items, people responsible, and project completion dates. You will also identify associated communication activities, including forms, worksheets, and visuals you will need to get started.

The Lean Primer has concise explanations and examples of many typical Lean concepts and tools. It will provide the foundation on which to build your Lean system.

The Lean Primer

Introduction

"The customer is always right." Is that really true? A small-town super-market owner in southern Connecticut believes it so much that when you enter the front door, the first thing you see is a huge granite stone with the following words chiseled into it:

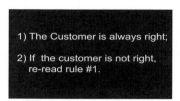

This isn't a marketing gimmick. Customers can return anything to this supermarket, no questions asked, even if the item wasn't purchased there. And when customers began breaking open packages of strawber-ries to sample them, the staff complained, but the owner said the follow-ing: "The customer is always right. Don't package the strawberries. Let people sample as many as they want to." The result? Happier cus-tomers and over a 1000% increase in sales of strawberries. No, that's not a typo. Sales increased by 1000%. In addition, there was a decrease in material and labor costs. The customer was right.

Many readers may think this only applies to the service industry, not to a factory. But Lean believers know it does apply to a factory. How does this philosophy translate to the shop floor? How does it save money, reduce cost, and help managers run a manufacturing business? Lean Manufacturing is the way.

Lean Manufacturing shortens the time it takes to convert customer orders into quality deliveries. With that thought in mind, it's easy to see that the primary goals of Lean are:

1. On-time deliveries; of a
2. Quality product; at the
3. Lowest possible cost (and lowest price) to the customer.

Management is constantly under pressure from customers to reduce price and lead times and to maintain the highest quality. Traditional thinking dictates that companies set sale prices by calculating costs and adding a margin of profit. But in today's economic environment, this method is a problem. There is always someone ready to offer a lower price.

The Lean Primer

What is required is cost reduction. Determine the price customers are willing to pay, and subtract the cost to determine what the profit will be at that cost level. This "Lean thinking" of price minus cost = profit forces a company to reduce costs within the organization (and supplier base) to ensure profit. The customer decides the price.

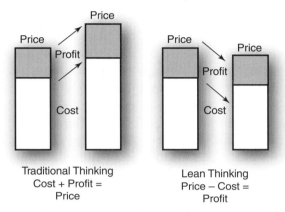

Traditional Thinking
Cost + Profit =
Price

Lean Thinking
Price – Cost =
Profit

Is this possible? It is if people apply Lean Thinking to their operations. This dictates that a customer gets what's needed, when it is needed. No more and no less. Anything that does not add value to a product is seen as waste and should be eliminated. This applies to internal customers as well as external customers.

That's why it is so important to look at reducing waste as the primary method of serving customers and maximizing profits. The basis of Lean Manufacturing is the absolute elimination of waste. Adding value and eliminating waste are the two sides of a coin. They are the reasons for implementing Lean Manufacturing.

Who Will Benefit

The Lean Primer provides information for understanding and planning how Lean manufacturing can work in various manufacturing environments such as: job shops, small shops, made-to-order, and low volume shops. Here are some guidelines to more clearly identify the audience for the *Running Lean*^{tm} series:

Job Shop
A "one-off" manufacturer of a high variety of parts or part types. Most orders are for one part. Some orders can be for multiple parts, but quantities are never high as related to cycle time. A job shop is distinguished by the single or main technology it employs. Job shops are typically a low-volume and high product mix. Some examples are aerospace plants, design engineering or test facilities, chemical processing plants, machine shops, a paint shops, or molding shops.

Small shop or small manufacturer
Any manufacturing operation with less than 250 employees

Discrete manufacturer
A custom order, common product manufacturer

Non-repetitive manufacturer
A whole class of manufacturing in which the product produced changes frequently or with each order. Any manufacturing other than assembly line manufacturing.

Make-to-order manufacturer
The product is manufactured only after an actual order is received. This is normally done because the cost of a product is too high to stock, or it has too many variations to build ahead according to a sales forecast. The product is usually pre-engineered prior to the order, but requires custom configuration. The component parts may be from stock or made specifically for an order. For example, foundries or engineered catalog products such as pumps, valves, control panels, and cylinders.

Engineering-to-order manufacturer

The product is custom engineered to an order. The product normally requires a high level of customization requested by the customer for each order. The product class is usually a high capital cost item or system. The engineering can consist of some pre-engineered modules, but will require some new engineering for each order. The component parts or systems are usually not stocked. They are ordered for the job due to high variations in specifications and usage volumes. The lead-times are typically months long. Examples:

- Die and mold machines (injection molding, stamping, die casting, or automatic foundry machines)
- Stamping and forming dies, plastic injection molds, die casting dies, etc.
- Checking and holding fixtures
- Automation builders (automated assembly lines, assembly fixtures, or assembly work stations)
- Large site-build equipment (steel mill, power generation, or paint- line)
- Construction companies (buildings, waste treatment, facilities, or roads)
- Steel fabricators
- Prototype shops

Focused factory

A facility or area within a facility dedicated to one product family. A product family is a small group of products that are very much alike and typically require the same manufacturing process steps. Example: cut, weld, paint, wire, assemble, and ship.

Short run or small lot manufacturer

Repetitive manufacturer who makes part runs as small as three parts to as large as several hundred parts to a specific order before changing over the production equipment for the next order. The orders can be individually bid or may be on a long term contract where the specific job order is a restocking release that may occur several times per month or year. Examples include: machined components that go into engineered catalog products, components for aircraft, medical, or the defense industry where annual volumes are relatively low.

Who
Will Benefit

If your operation is similar to any of the previously listed manufacturers, *The Lean Primer* and the *Running Lean*™ series were written for you!

The road to Lean is viewed as a continuous journey on which the producer is constantly striving to reach a destination of world-class status. The investment in time to meet and plan, communicate to employees, benchmark, re-design cells, and reorganize plants will have associated costs, but the costs must be viewed as an investment in the future of the business. The figure shown below is a fairly good representation of the balance between time and unit cost as related to costs and savings.

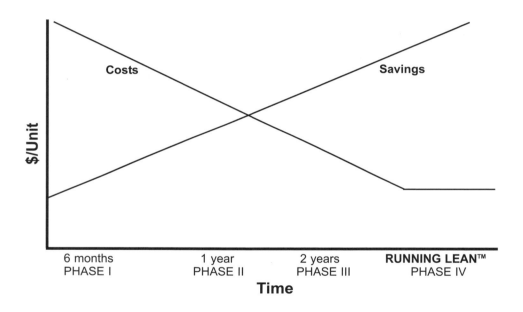

Lean Building Blocks

To achieve World Class status, a Lean system must stand on two pillars: Just-In-Time (JIT) and Jidoka or "built-in quality." But the pillars are not enough. The foundation on which the pillars rest is people and their role in the elimination of waste.

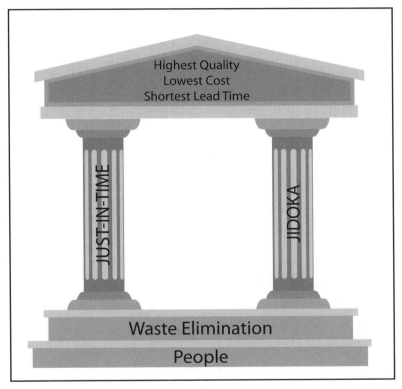

The Toyota Production System Model

Building Blocks

People: Creating a Favorable Environment For Lean

It would be nice if a manager could turn on a machine and have Lean Manufacturing automatically occur. Unfortunately, this is not reality. Reality is people working together toward a common goal, and that means acquiring tools and techniques that promote effective meetings, strong teams, and ongoing communication. In short, to implement Lean, a company must create a favorable environment for growth.

Rapid Response Meetings at the point of the problem must include people closest to the action. They solve problems within one hour of detection.

Building Blocks

Favorable work environments are obvious. They can be felt. It's not easy to figure out exactly how a favorable environment for Lean is created because there are reasons that are unique to each company, but there are usually common characteristics. They include:

- No blame attitude
- Clear leadership and direction, with a great deal of participation from everyone
- Creative ideas flowing from front line workers
- Trust and respect always being developed
- Training, learning, and communicating are high priorities
- There are many types of teams
- Managers are always involved in positive ways

To sustain Lean, a company must use Total Employee Involvement (TEI) to tap into all levels of knowledge and experience in the organization. TEI links specific knowledge into a cross-section of best practices and management support. TEI is a powerful force.

Visual measurements and positive recognition keep people involved.

Favorable Environment

There have been literally hundreds of scientific studies showing that people learn and function better in groups than they do alone. People are also likely to be more satisfied with their work and more motivated when working in a group.

When people come to work and are just told to "do your job", alienation, problems, and mistakes are more likely to occur. This does not provide a good foundation for creating a favorable environment.

Isolation does not promote learning or compliance to standards. It saps human energy. Teamwork, on the other hand, encourages learning, growth, and involvement. That's why Total Employee Involvement (TEI) is a key to Lean Manufacturing and should happen at all levels of the organization.

Open communication with facts is critical to Lean success.

Many issues can be resolved with honest dialogues.

Just-In-Time: Production On Demand

The first pillar of the Lean Manufacturing System is Just-In-Time (JIT) production. JIT provides customers with the quality product they ordered in a very specific way:

- Only those units ordered
- Just when they are needed
- In the exact amount needed

This applies not only to finished goods, but to all materials delivered to the next user or "internal customer" within the order-to-delivery process. If JIT is realized in the entire factory, then unnecessary inventories, both finished goods and work in process, will be eliminated. The inventory carrying costs will be diminished and profit will be increased.

Rules of Just-In-Time

1. Downstream processes withdraw items from upstream processes.
2. Upstream processes produce only what is withdrawn.
3. Shipping (everyone) sends only 100% defect-free products.
4. Kanban cards move with goods to provide visual control.
5. Continue to reduce number of kanbans.
6. Eliminate variation in flow at different processes.
7. Continue to shorten process and lead times.
8. Schedules should be flexible.

JIT cannot be accomplished through central planning, which informs all production schedules at the same time. Instead, it is necessary to look at what is called a "Pull" system, in which people in a certain process (downstream) go to the preceding process (upstream) to withdraw the necessary units in the necessary quantities at the required time. Then, the upstream process only produces enough quantities of units to replace those that have been withdrawn downstream.

It is incorrect to think that these quantities must exist in a "one piece flow" orientation. There are times when small batches are more efficient. The important thing is to serve the customer need while only producing what is needed when it is needed.

The Lean Primer

Jidoka: Building Quality into Production

The second pillar of Lean Manufacturing is Jidoka, sometimes referred to as "autonomation," or automation with a "human touch." The goal of Jidoka is "zero defects", to never pass a defective product downstream and to eliminate the risk that an undetected defect will end up in the hands of the customer. However, zero defects is not enough when it comes to Jidoka. Jidoka must be done in a way that promotes JIT and continuous flow.

Put another way, Jidoka's purpose is to achieve zero defects within a JIT system. Every step and task of improvement using the Jidoka principle accomplishes both goals.

> **The Three Functions of Jidoka**
>
> 1) Separate human work from machine work.
>
> 2) Develop defect-prevention devices.
>
> 3) Apply Jidoka to assembly operations.

Jidoka is different than automation. It is accomplished slowly, systematically, and inexpensively. It ensures that machines don't just move parts and products. Instead, machines in a Jidoka system do only "value-added" work, reduce cycle time, and prevent such waste as waiting, moving things, inspection, and defects. Further, Jidoka makes it easy to change any production process, while automation is difficult and expensive to change.

The Lean Primer

Overview of the Contents

Lean cannot be implemented unless the workers have a thorough understanding of it. The various tools and concepts that are explained in this book provide for that understanding.

Each section of the book represents one of three stages of understanding Lean. We highly recommend a Lean Assessment to be completed prior to any Lean implementation efforts. Visit **www.theleanstore.com** to preview *The Lean Assessment for Job Shops and Small Manufacturers.*

Introduction
This creates a basic understanding of the building blocks of Lean and how people fit into the process.

STABILIZE - STAGE I
In Stage One management must ensure that it is capable of serving the customer. Every employee must understand customer demand and why her or she must serve that demand. This employee must then implement temporary solutions that will remedy problems. At this time it will also begin to remove workplace barriers through the 5S System.

FLOW - STAGE II
Stage Two is the core of Lean implementation. Continuous flow manufacturing is implemented so that both internal and external customers receive the right product, at the right time, and in the right quantity.

SUSTAIN - STAGE III
Stage Three distributes work evenly by volume and variety to allow smaller orders, reduction in process variations, and elimination of mistakes. At this point, Total Employee Involvement is attained. Maintenance of machines and processes through visual controls becomes a primary focus.

THE FUTURE OF LEAN
Finally, there must be realization that Lean efforts and initiatives are ongoing as long as an organization's management desires to stay in today's business environment. Continued success and results obtained in the Lean journey will be the increasing rewards along the way.

Section Overview

Stage I begins by transforming the workplace into a place where change can actually occur. This is done through the 5 Steps of Workplace Organization and Transformation. If one message sinks in during this activity, it should be that "the status quo is no longer acceptable!" The 5S System involves everyone and removes barriers to Lean implementation.

The next step is to use specific measures and techniques to determine customer demand. As soon as customer demand has been determined, production must make the commitment to meet the demand immediately. Customers can't wait. They need quality product on time.

Stabilization is about preparing for change and meeting demand as soon as possible. It creates the foundation for the implementation of Lean methods. The following steps outline the process for implementing Stage I:

1. Create the Lean vision.
2. Obtain a snapshot of current material and information flow by creating a value stream or process map.
3. Establish a robust 5S or housekeeping system.
4. Match production capacity to sales and communicate the takt time to operators.
5. Ensure customer demand is being met daily, if not hourly, through the use of buffer and safety inventory.

Total Employee Involvement and ongoing training are crucial during Stage I.

The True Spirit of Lean

Lean Vision: The True Spirit of Lean

Everyone in your entire organization must truly believe that at some point in the future you may be able to reach the ideal state. To maintain the true spirit of Lean, you must continuously challenge each compromise that you make for practical reasons. To do this, you must maintain the vision of designing a process that will achieve one-piece flow and the elimination of all waste. This vision is called the "Lean Vision."

Lean Vision is always based on customer need and then translated into production quantities (takt time), quality (zero defects), or service (100% on-time delivery). For example, if management truly believes that customer demand is the driver for production, it will translate demand into takt time. If a production line's takt time requires that it produce one unit every 60 seconds, the Lean Vision is the view of how every part the organization can work to achieve providing that one unit every 60 seconds while maintaining zero defects. Put another way, an organization will achieve true continuous flow based on takt time. If everyone continues to work toward that vision every day, a Lean organization can be created.

The binding image is the Lean Vision. All companies must have a binding image.

Employees commit to vision by signing a company wide visual.

Metrics posted and updated regularly are important for the vision.

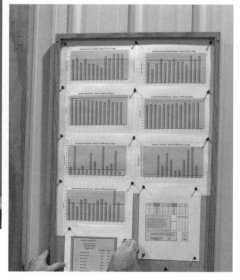

The Basics of Lean

Waste Elimination: The Basics of Lean

In Lean Manufacturing, all goals and measurements are based on the elimination of waste. The elimination of waste is the improvement activities in both the manufacturing arena and the front office.

How can employee's identify waste? Waste in manufacturing is everything that increases the cost of product without adding to its value. Waste elimination can be applied to any and all processes within an organization. By eliminating waste, step-by-step, in many small ways, costs can be significantly reduced. The result is dramatic savings and an increase in capacity.

Most companies find that only about 5% of activities are value-added and the rest are non value-added, or wasted activities. World Class organizations operate at a level above 40% value-added activity.

Lean Manufacturing has identified seven categories of waste that comprise the bulk of unnecessary costs in manufacturing. They are called the "Seven Areas of Waste." Understanding waste elimination is the foundation for establishing goals and measures that will provide cost-effective results.

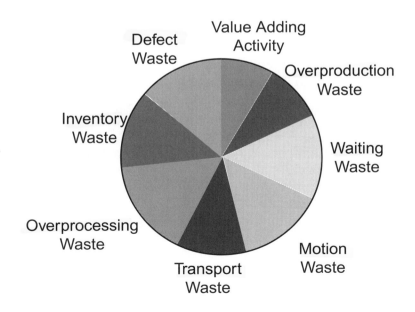

Waste:
The Basics of Lean

The Seven Areas of Waste

1. Overproduction

Overproduction is the worst of all waste. It is producing more of any-thing than is required to meet customer demand or producing it at a faster pace than is necessary. Overproduction tends to hide production problems or defects, workload fluctuations, and production inefficiencies. It is a wedge that holds the door open for other kinds of waste.

The root cause of overproduction is that machines and workers have excess capacity (waste) and put this excess capacity to work to turn out excess product.

> *To detect this waste, ask:*
>
> ✓ Is production faster or slower than takt time?
> ✓ Is there inventory in queue waiting for processing?
> ✓ Is there a lack of one-piece or small-lot flow?
> ✓ Is material presentation able to be improved?
> ✓ Is scheduling based on production quotas?
> ✓ Is there a lack of a pull system?
> ✓ Is takt time incorrect?
> ✓ Is the customer demand forecast incorrect?

2. Inventory

Excess stock of anything is waste. Excess inventory takes up space, requires people for movement and maintenance, may impact safety, and contributes to obsolescence if work requirements change.

> *To detect this waste, ask:*
>
> ✓ Are there queues everywhere?
> ✓ Are parts purchased or machined in larger quantities than customer demand?
> ✓ What is the amount of obsolete inventory?
> ✓ Is process capability poor?
> ✓ Is there a lack of properly sized and placed buffers?
> ✓ Is there standardized work and is it being followed?
> ✓ Is there too much variation in the manufacturing processes, machines, tools, or systems?
> ✓ Are setup time reduction methods being utilized to the fullest?

The Basics of Lean

3. Waiting

Any waiting by people, material, or machinery that does not add value is waste. Waiting waste can be created by poor equipment layout or poorly placed parts, dies and tools, causing more walking, reaching, or bending than necessary.

> *To detect this waste, ask:*
>
> ✓ Am I always watching the same operation and not adding value?
> ✓ Can something else be completed during any wait time?
> ✓ Is standardized work being followed?
> ✓ Is there a pull system in place?
> ✓ Are there buffers between processes? Are they the right quantity?
> ✓ Are kanbans being used?

4. Transport (conveyance)

Transport (conveyance) is an important element in production because it involves the delivery and movement of materials, information, and tools including the arrival of large batches of parts from suppliers. Any conveyance is waste because it does not add value. Transporting goods further than necessary or temporarily locating, restacking, and moving them is waste.

> *To detect this waste, ask:*
>
> ✓ Are parts/supplies moved and stored in inventory?
> ✓ Is plant layout optimized?
> ✓ Is transfer of parts fully automated?
> ✓ Is there a pull system?
> ✓ Is production machinery flexible?
> ✓ Are setup time reduction methods being utilized to the fullest?

5. Overprocessing   *Duplication of effort?*

Putting more work or effort into a task than is required is waste. This includes unnecessary checks and inspections. Excessive processing does not add value for the customer, and the customer will not pay for it. This can be the most difficult waste to uncover.

> *To detect this waste, ask:*
>
> ✓ What is the basic function of this procedure and part?
> ✓ Is the process design poor?
> ✓ Are there incorrect machine or process capability specifications?
> ✓ Is there a clear understanding of customer requirements?
> ✓ Do part specifications match customer requirements exactly?

6. Motion

Any movement by people or machinery that does not add value is motion waste. Ineffective job processes and poor plant designs are often responsible for creating more walking, reaching, or bending than necessary. Also included in this category is waiting. While one person performs unnecessary motion, another person or a piece of equipment is usually waiting. Waiting or searching for anything; tools, people, paper, machines, or information is waste. Waiting means that there is idle time that causes workflow stoppage.

> *To detect this waste, ask:*
>
> ✓ Can walking be reduced?
> ✓ Can body movement at any tasks be reduced?
> ✓ Can items be moved closer at the value added location?
> ✓ Can the workstation or area benefit from cellular layout?
> ✓ Are proper kaizen techniques in use?
> ✓ Is there a thorough 5S program?
> ✓ Is standard work being performed?
> ✓ Is cross-training being done?

7. Correction (of Defects)

This category of waste refers to all extra processing needed to correct defects. The production work should have been performed correctly the first time. Defects result in scrap as well as the expenditure of unnecessary time, materials, energy, equipment, and labor. These include final inspections, which should not be necessary if work is performed correctly the first time.

To detect this waste, ask:

What is the defect rate?
Are there common reasons for defects?
Are master parts available?
Is inventory hiding defects?
Is there a lack of process capability of machines, tools, or techniques?
Is standardized work being followed?
Are defects accurately being determined by specifications or by perceptions?

Keys to Waste Elimination

★ Development of current and future state value stream maps

★ Reduction in travel for parts, paper, and people

★ Reduction in inventories (raw material, WIP, finished goods)

★ Consider an eighth waste of people utilization

Proper cell design will assist greatly in reducing many wastes.

Cost Reduction Opportunities

Value Stream Mapping: Identifying Cost Reduction Opportunities

Value Stream Mapping is a tool that reveals the flow of material and information as a product makes its way through a process. Following the ordering and production path from beginning to end and carefully drawing a visual representation of every process in the material and information flow creates a Current State Map. Then, by asking a set of questions about how production should flow, and drawing it, a Future State Map or proposed plan can be created.

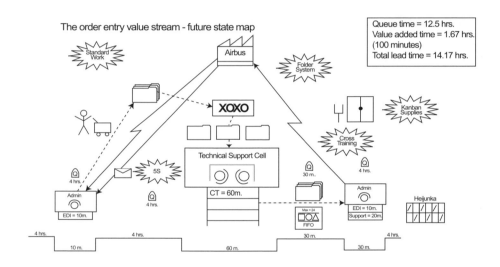

Value stream maps are used to create current and future states with a standard set of icons.

Cost Reduction Opportunities

The Value Stream Mapping tool is useful if used within a systematic approach to Lean implementation. Other mapping or facility layout exercises don't lend themselves to identify sources of waste or obstacles to production flow. Value Stream Mapping will:

- Create a common vision for everyone connected to the focus area
- Provide a visual map for ease of communication
- Allow waste to be identified by everyone so improvements can be determined
- Provide the foundation to implement Lean initiatives from the customer's perspective

Keys to Value Stream Mapping

★ Value Stream Mapping is a valuable part of a systematic approach to Lean implementation. It should not be used in isolation.

★ Include all aspects of a value stream, including order entry, production scheduling, material shipping, and product shipping.

★ Get key people involved and share the map with everyone - not just management.

★ Create the Current and Future State Maps on a whiteboard or flipchart for everyone to see.

★ Follow through by having the right people involved and ensuring that there is communication and ongoing improvement.

★ Create an implementation plan of activities to move from the current state to a future state.

★ Develop metrics to track progress.

Workplace Organization

5S: Workplace Organization and Transformation

The 5S System contains five steps for organizing and transforming the workplace. The name for each step begins with the letter "S." 5S removes workplace obstacles that prevent Lean implementation from occurring. 5S also eliminates waste at the source where it forms and accumulates.

The Basic 5S System

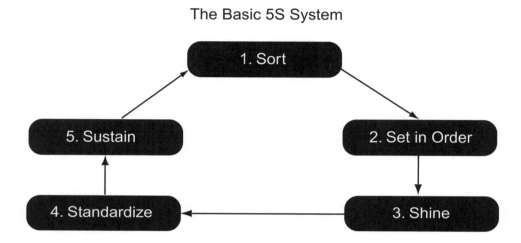

Workplace Organization

1. Sort

Sort involves reviewing the contents of an area and removing unnecessary items. The real meaning of Sort is found in the saying, "When in doubt, move it out." A temporary holding area is essential for success.

The photo on the left is a staging area after cells were sorted.

Both large and small tools should be sorted and organized.

Supplies for cells or work areas can be centralized if runners are utilized.

29

5S:
Workplace Organization

2. Set in Order

Set in Order or "straighten" involves arranging necessary items for easy and efficient access and keeping them that way. The essence of Set in Order is found in the saying, "A place for everything, and everything in its place." The primary tools for Set in Order are lines, labels, and signs.

Tooling, etc. should be labeled at point-of-use.

Administrative areas are just as important to 5S!

3. Shine

Shine involves keeping everything clean and using cleaning as a way to ensure that the area and equipment are maintained as they should be. The essence of Shine is found in the saying, "Make it clean, leave it clean." After initial cleaning is performed, those who use an area must perform some cleaning on a daily basis.

Floors cleaned properly impress customers.

The type of floor surface does not matter - any type can look good.

4. Standardize

Standardize involves creating guidelines for keeping the area organized, orderly, and clean, and making the standards visual and obvious. The essence of Standardize is found in the saying, "If you can't see, you don't know, and if you don't know, you can't control."

The primary tools for the fourth S are visual displays and visual controls.

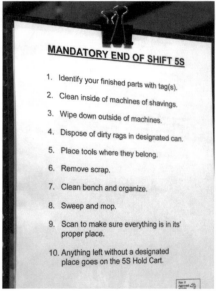

Ensure both shifts work from the same set of standards.

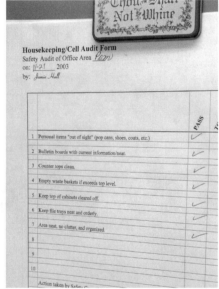

Cell audits should be created to the standards set.

5. Sustain

Sustain involves education and communication to ensure that everyone follows the 5S standards. The essence of Sustain is found in the saying, "Sustain all gains through self-discipline." But to maintain self-discipline, standards must be in place, they must be obvious, everyone must understand them, and they must be continuously reinforced.

Create visual controls to assist in sustaining workplace organization.

Involve team/cell leaders for audits.

Keys to 5S

★ Support and involvement required from management

★ 5S is the foundation for other Lean tools and practices

★ Don't make it "flavor of the month"; ensure it as part of job requirement

★ Develop a scoring method to track progress in each area

★ Most of all, make it fun

Takt Time:
Matching Demand with Production

Takt Time: Matching Customer Demand with Production

Takt time determines how fast a process needs to run to meet customer demand. Takt is a German word for a musical beat or rhythm. Just as a metronome keeps the beat for music, takt time keeps the beat for customer demand. Takt time is the time required between completion of successive units of end product. For example, at a drive shaft line in a screw machine shop, twelve seconds may be required at the end of the line between each unit's completion to meet demand. This establishes a takt time of twelve seconds. A part should be completed every twelve seconds. It should be emphasized that takt time is based on customer demand, not on machine capability.

Takt time is useful as a planning tool for jobs. For each job, takt time will tell people whether they can meet customer demand. Knowing whether you can meet demand is like seeing into the future. You can change machine cycle times, personnel, the number of shifts, or even process flow to meet demand. Takt time makes this possible.

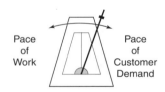

Pace of Work

Pace of Customer Demand

Takt Time Formula

$$\text{Takt Time} = \frac{\text{Available Production Time}}{\text{Required Daily Production Quantity}} = \frac{\text{Time}}{\text{Volume}}$$

Note: For high volume value streams it helps to calculate takt time in seconds.

Takt Time:
Matching Demand with Production

To calculate takt time for a particular value stream, line, or cell, divide the available daily production time by the total quantity required for one day. Remember to use only available (i.e., paid) production time. If a shift is listed as 8.5 hours, but there is a 30 minute unpaid lunch, the total available time is 8 hours.

Parts counter at the end of line where actual production is compared to scheduled or "takt" amount.

Keys to Takt Time

★ Acknowledges customer demand numerically to everyone

★ Creates flexibility as demand increases and decreases

★ Assists in need for cross-training

★ Improves flow and throughput

Buffer and Safety Stock: Meeting Customer Demand Now

Once customer demand has been determined, producers must meet it immediately. An organization cannot wait until Lean Manufacturing is completely implemented. It can, however, confidently meet demand with current production processes, with the use of buffer and safety stock. These are temporary measures that help meet demand while implementing Lean improvement plans.

Buffer and Safety Stock	
Buffer Stock:	Finished goods avilable to meet customer demand due to variations in customer ordering patterns.
Safety Stock:	Finished goods available to meet customer demand due to internal constraints or inefficiencies.
Note:	These inventories should be stored and tracked separately. They exist for two distinct reasons.

By establishing buffer and safety stock, an organization can meet demand without requiring overtime on an irregular basis. But remember that buffer and safety stock is a **compromise** to the Lean system. As customer demand becomes more stable and internal efficiencies improve, these inventories should be reviewed and eventually eliminated.

Keys to Buffer and Safety Stock

★ Support importance of meeting customer demand

★ Work towards keeping inventories to a minimum

★ Ensure first-in, first-out type replenishment process

★ Can be used to level production

Customer Demand Now

Finished Goods Supermarket

Finished goods should be stored in a Finished Goods Supermarket.

Shipping personnel are responsible to ensure products are shipped, but they are not solely responsible for meeting customer demand. The entire value stream has that responsibility. Shipping personnel must be able to withdraw finished goods from some source and ship them to the customer. Often that source is located at the end of a line, not in the shipping department. This is called a "Finished Goods Supermarket."

This Finished Goods Supermarket allows shipping to remove the quantity of product needed when ordered by the customer. The picking and the replacement that accompanies the supermarket is managed like any supermarket. It is a system in which an item is not replaced until it is removed.

Finished Goods Supermarkets should be easily accessible to the runner or the shipping department.

Keys to Finished Goods Supermarket

★ Replacement of removed products should be quickly communicated upstream

★ Keep inventories to a minimum

★ Ensure first-in, first-out type replenishment process

★ Ensure area is part of 5S

Ask Yourself

Ask Yourself:

1. Is there a true "Binding Vision" for Lean? Is management completely involved? Has the vision been communicated to everyone in the company?

2. What items in the workplace are needed, and what can be removed?

3. Where does contamination exist, and where is cleaning needed?

4. Are all items and equipment located where they should be?

5. Are we overproducing, under-producing, or meeting demand?

6. Can we meet demand with current production capabilities?

7. Do we need buffer and/or safety stock? Can we eliminate overtime?

Personal Notes

Personal Notes:

Describe the typical worker's knowledge of Lean and meeting customer demand:

Describe barriers in the organization that need to be overcome to be more pro-active in Lean initiatives:

List people who can work to ensure customer demand is met:

List potential team members who would contribute to the improvement of meeting customer demand by ensuring 100% on-time-delivery (do not overlook what the front offices can do to assist in this):

List action items, including who is responsible for completion.

Comments:

Summary

Summary

Gaining a basic understanding of meeting customer demand will permit the first wave of changes to occur. Employees will contribute and actively support any and all 5S or Housekeeping initiatives, and from that platform of success, continue on the Lean path.

Terms to Review

Stabilize , Lean Vision, Waste, Value Stream Mapping, 5S, Takt Time, Buffer Stock, Safety Stock, Finished Goods Supermarket

Directions

1. Review the Reality Check section including the Personal Notes.

2. Start generating a list of ideas for activities.

3. For each activity, identify who is responsible, a start and completion date, and any additional information required (i.e., tools, training, communication, etc.).

Call to Action

Use a similar form to the sample Call to Action on the accompanying page and create a list of activities for planning and organizing Lean practices within your organization.

Sample Call to Action

Call to Action				
Target Area Side Arm - AB Intl.	**Date** 3/15			
Lean Activity	Person Responsible	Start Date	Materials/People & Comments	Completion Date
Ensure entire staff reads and understands The Lean Primer	John	3/15	Acquire 5 copies of The Lean Primer	3/31
Gather customer demand data	Susan/Bob	3/15	Ensure info is catergorized	3/31

Keys to Stabilize

★ 5S and people are the foundation for Lean

★ Be creative when value stream or process mapping. If you require additional icons, create them.

★ Monitor buffer and safety resources to continually minimize

★ Spend the necessary time to understand customer demand

Create Flow

Section Overview

In Stage II, people apply the core of Lean Manufacturing: continuous flow. The primary objective of Stage II is to ensure that the next down-stream process has:

Only those units needed,
Just when they are needed,
In the exact amount needed.

For this to happen the workplace must be organized and clean. The required tools for producing customer demand must be in place so that improvement will occur without interrupting regular, timely deliveries to the customer.

The following steps outline the process for implementing Stage II.

1. Perform line balancing - determine optimal distribution of work elements in the production stream to meet demand.
2. Establish standard work for all key processes, both manufact-uring and non-manufacturing.
3. Re-design the production areas using flow design.
4. Shorten lead times and machine down time, especially through quick changeovers.
5. Determine how to control production through use of kanban, supermarkets, and visual controls.
6. Ensure quality through mistake proofing.

Creating flow is ensuring a balance between worker production efficien-cy and customer demand. This is the heart of a Lean system. Total Employee Involvement and ongoing training continue to be crucial dur-ing Stage II.

Continuous Flow:
Designing for Smooth Work Flow

Continuous Flow: Designs for a Smooth Work Flow

An uninhibited work flow is the most important issue in designing a production process. To maximize efficiency and serve customer demand a producer must achieve an efficient flow. Flow encompasses the overall stream of production, including raw material, machining, and assembly, as well as in individual operations, for example positioning a part, tightening screws, packaging, or taping a box. Flow even includes support operations such as tool delivery or information acquisition.

Parts must travel one after the other through the work sequence in a smooth, continuous flow. To achieve this, equipment is sequenced to sustain flow, not in machine or process groups. Arranging equipment in groups, or by function, usually prevents flow by creating bottlenecks of material and product.

Failure to arrange equipment in accordance with work sequence results in a number of wastes, including:

- Accumulation of work in process (WIP) after each machine or operation
- Excessive conveyance between operations
- Excessive material handling time (3 to 5 times as much)
- Slow detection and correction of defects resulting in higher scrap and rework
- Long production lead times
- Slow production of final product
- More workers needed for lower production quantities

One method to achieve continuous flow is called one-piece flow or small lot flow. In this method, each operation is arranged next to each other, in sequence, for non-interrupted flow. The piece is passed from one operation to the next until it is completed, one piece at a time (or small lot at a time). The advantages to one-piece flow include:

- A drastic reduction in WIP
- Immediate correction of defects resulting in lower scrap and rework
- Zero conveyance between operations
- Drastic reduction in material handling
- Faster production and a reduction in lead times
- More than 50% reduction in floor space
- Greater work capacity

Designing for Smooth Work Flow

One-piece flow is not always practical in plants that use dies or molds or perform molding, casting, forging, or stamping. However, continuous flow principles still apply in these plants. For example, some large machines can be integrated into assembly lines.   A product that must travel through five stamping machines can possibly be arranged in a row, each stamping one piece at a time, resulting in a finished piece (eliminating WIP at each machine).

Cell Design

The idea of cell design comes from a principle called multi-process handling. In multi-process handling, a worker performs various operations to move items through the production sequence. For example, the worker may use a lathe, a mill, a drill, a grinder, and may then wash and package the part.

Principles of Cell Layout

Sequential arrangement of processes.

Last operation placed close to first.

Flexible equipment (small equipment, wheels, easy to move, etc.).

Machines positioned close together, with safety taken into consideration in reference to material and hand movement.

Multi-process handling allows flexibility. Personnel can be adjusted to meet changing production requirements without compromising productivity. Workers can be cross-trained to perform many types of operations. Equipment can be designed for quick and easy exchange.

Multi-process design is often called cell design. A work cell is a self-contained unit that includes several value-adding operations. The cell will have the equipment and personnel arranged in process sequence. Cells perform all the operations necessary to complete a product or a major production sequence. By arranging operations into cells, operators can produce and transfer parts one piece at a time with improved safety and reduced effort.

Designing for Smooth Work Flow

Keep product demand and mix in mind when designing the cell layout. The cell must be able to adapt to handle the changing demands of the customer.

Create cells that are easily identified by floor markings or signs.

Create cells easily accessible for pick-up and drop-off of materials and finished parts.

Keys to Continuous Flow

- ★ Understanding customer demand thoroughly will provide a good foundation

- ★ Multi-functional operators/workers are developed to maintain flow

- ★ Processes should be located as close together as possible without compromising safety

- ★ WIP is kept to a minimum

Finding the Best Way to Do a Job

Standard Work: Finding the Best Way to do a Job

Standard Work means establishing and using only the best procedures to perform a job. It achieves confidence and control because managers and workers create the standards together. It provides a method for maintaining high levels of productivity, quality, and safety. For consistent high levels of performance to occur, everyone needs to know that work will be done the same way, regardless of who is doing it.

> **Standard Work**
>
> Standard Work is an agreed-upon set of work procedures that establish the best method and sequence for each process.
>
> Note: You can use Standard Work Charts to illustrate the sequence of operations within a process, including the cycle times of the operations. This should be posted in the area.

Standard Work will determine the best flow of work, taking into account quality, quantity, cost, and safety. The goal of Standard Work is to maintain the flow of work, based on customer demand, and to maintain an optimal work load for each employee. It's important to note that employees should never be overloaded when demand increases. Likewise, when demand decreases, or processes are streamlined, fewer workers are assigned to a line. So Takt Time is an important element in Standard Work as is working sequence (described in cell design) and standard in-process stock.

Standard Work utilizes three main tools:

- ➡ Standard Work Combination Table
- ➡ Standard Work Chart
- ➡ Operator Instruction Sheet

Standard Work:
Finding the Best Way to Do a Job

The Standard Work Combination Table

To gain an accurate assessment of any process that requires manual or a combination of manual and automatic operations, a work team must complete a Standard Work Combination Table. The Standard Work Combination Table:

- Indicates the flow of human work within an operation
- Documents the exact time requirement for each work step or element
- Displays the job design sequence based on takt time (customer demand)
- Demonstrates the time relationship between manual work, machine work, and movement (or walk time)

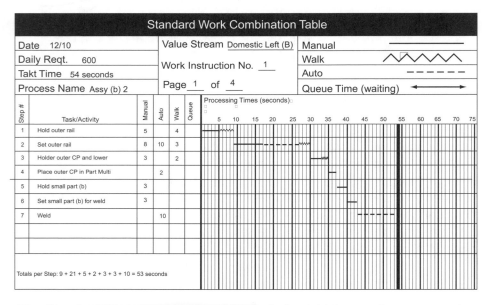

The Standard Work Combination Table includes takt time and process cycle times.

The Standard Work Combination Table is an important tool for allocating manpower and allowing management to check the production volume, judge the skills of each worker, and identify and solve problems.

Finding the Best Way to Do a Job

The Standard Work Chart

The Standard Work Chart is a diagram that illustrates the work sequence. It also shows Takt Time and in-process stock. Operators and supervisors refer to the Standard Work Chart frequently in connection with worksite operation and management. It will often be posted at the worksite. The Standard Work Chart:

- Displays the work sequence, process layout, and Work-In-Process
- Displays the operator movement for each work element for the operation
- Identifies quality, safety, or critical defect areas to be aware of

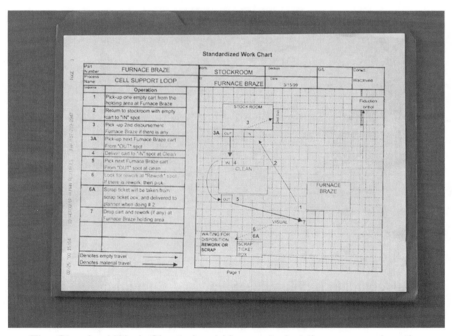

The Standard Work Chart should be posted at the process location.

Finding the Best Way to Do a Job

Operator Instruction Sheet

The first two forms are supported by the Standard Operator Instruction Sheet (OIS), which is primarily for training and ensuring adherence to standards. The OIS provides the opportunity to demonstrate the standard sequence in which the work should be done. There are a number of reasons for creating a Standard Operator Instructor Sheet:

- ➨ To provide an accurate set of instructions for training staff.
- ➨ To provide a list of instructions to follow as people complete their tasks.
- ➨ To allow management to confirm that standards are followed.
- ➨ To develop standards that will safely produce a quality product in the most efficient way within Takt Time.

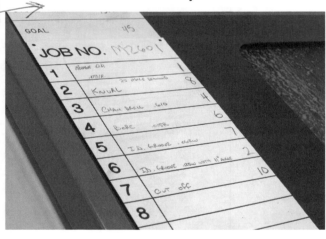

Operator instructions should be located close to the operation.

Keys to Standard Work

★ Videotaping is an accurate way to document the current processing sequence. It will also provide a baseline for continual improvement.

★ The tables and charts should be changed as necessary to improve safety, quality, or efficiency.

★ Tables and charts should be posted near the work area. They should also be reviewed on a regular basis.

★ Work together with operators to determine the most efficient work methods. Gain a consensus, otherwise compliance is unlikely.

Taking a Bite Out of Downtime

Quick Changeover: Taking a Bite Out of Downtime

By implementing takt time and continuous flow, it is likely that managers will also want to increase product variation and smaller lot sizes. The greatest single obstacle to increased variation is machine changeovers or set-ups. Changeover begins when the current process completes its final defect-free product, and ends when the next process creates its first defect-free product. During changeover, no product is being made. All of the time is non-value adding. It is waste.

> **Changeover Measurement**
>
> Changeover begins when the current process completes its final defect-free product, and ends when the next process creates its first defect-free product.

However, if changeovers can be performed quickly, it will allow production of greater product variety and more capacity. The benefits of Quick Changeovers are:

- The ability to produce a greater variety of parts
- A reduction of in-process inventory due to smaller lot sizes
- Operators being able to run multiple machines due to shorter changeover times
- Support of one-piece or small lot flow
- Reduction in lead times

> **When to Implement Quick Changeovers**
>
> During the stablilization stage, when changeovers prove to be a major obstacle in serving a customer.
>
> During the standardization stage, when changeovers play an important role in maintaining standard work and continuous flow.

Quick Changeover:
Taking a Bite Out of Downtime

Quick Changeover is a method that makes it possible to perform equipment setup and changeover operations in the minimum amount of time possible, sometimes under 10 minutes. It begins with a thorough analysis of the current changeover procedures. It is applied in three sequential stages:

1. Distinguish between "internal" changeover tasks that can be performed only while the machine is shut down and "external" changeover tasks that can be performed while the machine is running.

Ensure proper paper work (routers, etc.) are with the parts making up a job kit.

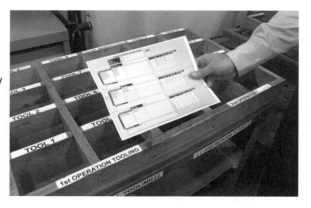

Organize tooling on carts or in a kit will assist greatly in reducing searching for parts.

Taking a Bite Out of Downtime

2. Convert internal tasks to external tasks when possible. Improve storage and management of parts and tools to streamline external setup operations.

Pre-staging and delivering tooling and materials before changeover begins can reduce setup times by 50%.

3. Streamline all setup activities by implementing parallel operations (dividing the work between two or more people) using functional clamping methods instead of bolts, thus eliminating adjustments and mechanizing when necessary.

Keys to Quick Changeovers

★ By addressing the obvious things, like preparing and transporting tools and equipment while the machine is still running, changeover times can be cut by up to 50 percent or more.

★ Assure a good scheduling system is in place.

★ Keep operators in their cells (areas) by providing necessary tools and materials required for the job.

★ Utilize videotaping for higher profile jobs and have operators evaluate their methods.

Pulling the Work

Kanban: Pulling Work through the Production Process

The "kanban" system is used to manage the flow of material throughout the factory. It can also be used as a method to regulate orders from the factory to suppliers.

The Origin of Kanban

Kanban, in Japanese, means "card", "billboard", or "sign." The term is often used synonymously for the card itself, and the inventory control system developed by the Toyota Production System.

Kanban lets the preceding process know when it withdraws a part and automatically triggers for its replenishment. It is strictly a "pull system." The product is produced and supplies are ordered only when a kanban card says to due so, not by schedule, but when products are used or "pulled."

There are three types of Kanban:

A *Production Kanban* is a printed card indicating the number of parts that need to be processed to replenish what was taken.

A *Withdrawal Kanban* is a printed card indicating the number of parts to be removed from the Supermarket and supplied downstream.

A *Signal Kanban* is a printed card indicating the reorder point has been attained and a particular material lot needs to be replenished.

Implementing Kanban

Rules of Kanbans

1. Downstream processes withdraw items from upstream processes.
2. Upstream processes produce only what is withdrawn.
3. Send only 100% defect-free products.
4. Kanban cards move with goods to provide visual control.
5. Continue to reduce number of kanbans.
6. Eliminate variation in flow at different processes.
7. Continue to shorten process and lead times.

Kanbans are created after a line or cell has been balanced and designed. It is the last step in the standardization and control of a process. There are a few rules that make the Kanban System effective:

A *Withdrawal Kanban* is a printed card indicating the number of parts to be removed from the Supermarket and supplied downstream.

Finished goods?   *shipped to cust?*

Store			Preceding Process
Shelf No. Item Back No.			
Item No.			
Item Name			
Car Type			
			Subsequent Process
Box Capacity	Box Type	Issue No.	

Kanban:
Pulling the Work

A *Production Kanban* is a printed card indicating the number of parts that need to be processed to replenish what was taken.

Store	Process
Shelf No.　　　Item Back No. _____	
Item No. _____	
Item Name _____	
Car Type _____	

A *Signal Kanban* is a printed card, usually triangular in shape, indicating that the reorder point has been attained and a particular material lot needs to be replenished.

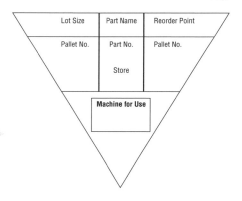

Lot Size	Part Name	Reorder Point
Pallet No.	Part No.	Pallet No.
	Store	
	Machine for Use	

Kanban cards should be easily placed to identify when to reorder

Supermarkets: A Discussion

Without Kanban, supermarkets are just a bunch of shelves, another way to store things. So, when references are made to a Supermarket System, it also means that Kanban is being used.

The supermarket used by shipping is called a "Finished Goods Supermarket." This Finished Goods Supermarket allows shipping to remove the quantity of product needed when ordered by the customer. The picking and replacement that accompanies a Finished Goods Supermarket is managed like any supermarket. It is a system in which an item is never replaced until it is removed.

This Finished Goods Supermarket at a specialty wire manufacturing plant is kanban controlled.

Where continuous flow is not possible, especially due to outsourcing (such as heat treating or plating), you can use an In-Process Supermarket system. A supermarket of work-in-process may be necessary to ensure that flow is possible. It can also be used when there are multiple demands made on a machine or a cell.

Pulling the Work

In-Process Supermarkets are used to schedule those upstream processes that cannot flow continuously. The need for Supermarkets should decrease as flow is improved. Supermarkets are a compromise to the ideal state. A company will not achieve its ideal state overnight, but keep the Lean Vision alive and continually work toward the ideal state.

Administrative areas can use folders as kanbans.

Kanbans should always be with the parts.

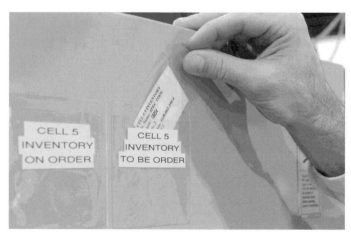

Kanbans should have a location when replenishment is required.

Kanban:
Pulling the Work

Keys to Kanban

★ Kanban is the heart of a Pull System.

★ Kanbans use standard containers or lot sizes with a single card attached to each. When the inventory represented by that card is used, the card acts as a signal to indicate that more inventory is needed. In this way, inventory is provided only when needed, in the standard amount needed.

★ Kanban cards always move with the goods to ensure "Just-In-Time information" and visual control at all times.

★ Quality must be built in at each process. Processes should never send any defective goods downstream.

★ Kanbans reduce inventory.

Creating a Visual Workplace

Visual Controls: Creating a Visual Workplace

The purpose of visual displays and controls is to gain compliance with all standards, not just standard operating procedures. These include physical workplace standards, tooling standards, performance standards, maintenance standards, and/or any rule or guideline that exists in the workplace.

The ideal for visual controls is that they are so completely integrated with action that deviation from standards is eliminated. In a factory, all displays and controls work together to form a visual language so that the factory may be regarded as a Visual Factory.

Type	General Purpose
Storyboards	Share information about projects or improvement. To education and motivate.
Signboards	Share vital information at point-of-use.
Maps	Share actual processes, standard operating procedures, directions, etc.
Kanbans	Control the withdrawal of work (or supplies) in and out of supermarkets, work areas, etc. Can be used to regulate FIFO lanes.
Checklists	Provide an operational tool that facilitates compliance with standards, procedures, etc.
Indicators, Color codes	Show correct location, item types, amount, or direction of flow.
Andons, Alarms	Provide a strong, unavoidable sign or signal where there is an abnormality or action to be taken (e-mail alert, pager code, etc.).

Visual Controls:
Creating a Visual Workplace

Storyboards

A storyboard is a graphic representation of holding key information for a Lean project. It communicates the progress and key information on a project as it unfolds.

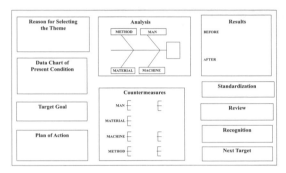

Teams should ensure story-boards are engaging by including color and data that is easy to understand.

Signboards

Signboards should be used to address locations of equipment, resources, and anything else that may be required to efficiently run a factory. Many times using signboards will become part of the facility addressing system.

Signboards are used to identify stocking location for bar stock.

Creating a Visual Workplace

Location Indicators

Another step in the development of a visual factory is the adoption and standardization of location indicators. This includes a plant-wide system for lines, labels, and even color-coding. The 5S System creates the foundation for location indicators but may not provide a plant-wide strategy. At some point, a plant must evolve into a visual workplace where everyone knows the visual language of lines, labels, and colors.

Lines designate aisles and location of equipment and secondary items.

Cabinets, as well as drawers, should be part of a facility address system.

Visual Controls:
Creating a Visual Workplace

Visual Metrics

The effective use of information depends on the reporting and display of that information. That's why Visual Metrics can be so helpful in the over-all implementation of a Lean System. Visual Metrics do the following:

- ➡ Make data easy for teams to understand and interpret
- ➡ Clarify the underlying loss picture
- ➡ Focus improvement activity

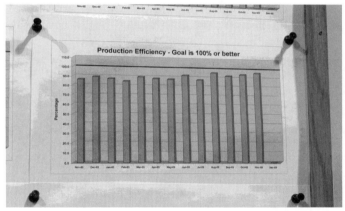

Bar charts are easy to read and show progress toward a goal.

A good visual metric will have the following characteristics:

- ➡ It is directly related to strategy or standard
- ➡ It is a non-financial measure
- ➡ The measure is location specific
- ➡ It is easy to use
- ➡ It provides fast feedback and fosters improvement

Involve workers in visual controls of often as possible.

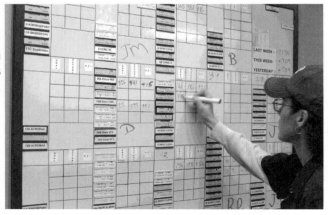

Visual Controls:
Creating a Visual Workplace

Visual Displays

Visual Displays are a method to visually communicate important information about the work environment, safety, operations, storage, quality, equipment, tools, improvement activities, and other work standards.

Displays of tool sets and storage locations allow for reduced setups.

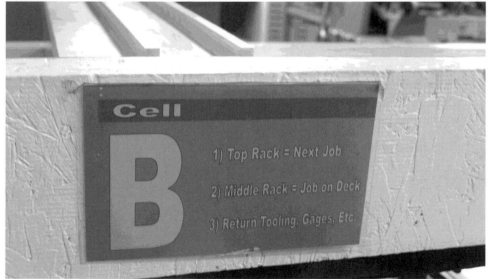

Visual displays can be used for operator instructions also.

Visual Controls:
Creating a Visual Workplace

The Visual Factory begins with one simple premise. "One picture is worth a thousand words." If that picture is available exactly when you need it, where you need it, with just the right amount of information, then it's worth *several* thousand words. The essence of the Visual Factory is "Just-In-Time information."

Visual displays should be at the point of use and make a clear statement.

Keys to Visual Controls

★ Visual Display and Control is an integral part of work area standardization.

★ Incorporate measurements as visual controls.

★ Make information easily accessible.

★ Once a visual control has been created, create a plan for review.

★ Include front office processes.

Mistake-Proofing: Achieving Zero Defects

The goal of mistake-proofing is zero defects, never to pass a defective product downstream, and to eliminate the risk that an undetected defect will end up in the hands of the customer. The principle of stopping work immediately whenever a defect or abnormality occurs is fundamental to Lean Manufacturing.

To achieve zero defects, production equipment and processes are designed to detect abnormalities and to stop automatically when detection occurs. In addition, workers are equipped with methods to stop production flow whenever they notice any errors or problems. This combination of mechanical and human mistake-proofing prevents defective parts from traveling to the next stage of production. It also prevents major equipment breakdowns.

Another advantage of mistake-proofing is that it shows the causes of problems by stopping the equipment exactly where the problem occurred and by calling attention to it with a signal or indicator.

The most important effect of mistake-proofing is the way it changes production management. Operators can spend more time in value-adding activities because they no longer have to watch for machine errors. Mistake-proofing devices do this task automatically. Operators become quality experts through self-inspection, saving wasted time.

Some Principles About Mistake-Proofing

In most operations the essential ingredient is people. People make errors. Errors lead to defects. No matter how much we wish to avoid making errors, sooner or later they will occur. While we tend to accept errors as something natural, we find fault with the people who made them. Mistake-proofing fixes the source of the mistake within the manufacturing system rather than blaming the person.

Mistake-Proofing Devices

There are three levels of control that mistake-proofing devices can achieve:

Level 1: Eliminate the error at the source before it occurs.

Level 2: Detect the error as it occurs, before it results in a defect.

Level 3: Detect the defect after it has been made, before it reaches the next process.

Mistake-Proofing:
Achieving Zero Defects

Errors can be eliminated. Any kind of error that people make can be prevented. People will tend to make fewer errors if their production system is based on the principle that errors can be prevented. It should regard people as the source of these solutions rather than the cause of the problems. The most effective way to prevent errors in a production system is through mistake-proofing devices.

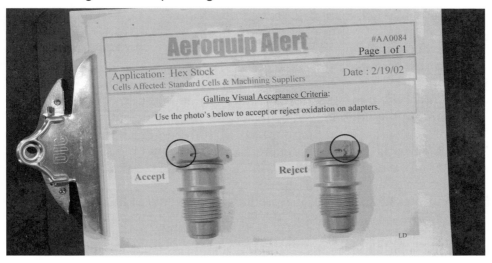

Mistake-Proofing should include the proper visual aides to educate employees.

Keys to Mistake-Proofing

★ Remember, the goal of mistake proofing is zero defects.

★ All operators must understand the principles of mistake-proofing and believe that any error can be prevented.

★ Look at the process, not the people, for the root cause of a mistake.

★ Mistake-proofing reduces cycle time and prevents waste such as waiting, inspection and, or course, defects.

★ Mistake-proofing can be in the form of physical devices, procedures, and software enhancements, to name a few.

Ask Yourself

Ask Yourself:

1. Do you have an accumulation of Work-In-Process (WIP) after each machine or assembly operation? If so, do you know how many days of on-hand inventory that creates?

2. Do you have conveyance between operations?

3. How much material handling time is within a process or total time to get a part through the facility?

4. Do you need more mistake-proofing devices to reduce defects? If so, where are they needed?

5. Are standards in place to ensure consistent work output and quality parts are being produced?

6. Are workers balanced to the production schedule of the day? Or hour?

7. Do you have kanbans in place for products and/or office supplies?

8. Can changeovers be improved?

Personal Notes

Personal Notes:

Describe the typical worker's knowledge of Lean and understanding continuous flow:

Describe barriers in the organization that need to be overcome to be more pro-active in Lean initiatives:

List areas that can work to improve the flow of material and information:

List potential team members who could contribute to the improvement of material within the facility (do not overlook what the front offices can do to assist in this):

List action items, including who is responsible for completion.

Comments:

Summary

Summary

Gaining a basic understanding of how the various Lean tools will improve material flow throughout the facility greatly enhances nearly all areas of measurements. There is quite a bit to the Flow Phase and it is critical not to rush too many Lean tools to the employees. Learn and implement one Lean tool or concept well and then quickly expand (implement) to other areas.

Terms to Review

Continuous Flow, Cell Design, Standard Work, Changeover, Location Indicators, Signboards, Kanban, In-Process Supermarket, Visual Display, Visual Control, Mistake-Proofing

Directions

1. Review the Reality Check section including the Personal Notes.

2. Start generating a list of ideas for activities.

3. For each activity, identify who is responsible, a start and completion date, and any additional information required (i.e., tools, training, communication, etc.).

Call to Action

Use a similar form to the sample Call to Action on the accompanying page and create a list of activities for planning and organizing Lean practices within your organization.

Call to Action

Call to Action				
Target Area Helm Product Line B **Date** 6/30				
Lean Activity	Person Responsible	Start Date	Materials/People & Comments	Completion Date
Establish team to reduce changeover time on Helm product line	Joe	6/30	Create standard work forms	7/15
Establish kanban with customer	Joyce/Dave	6/30	Benchmark local	7/30

Keys to Flow

★ Continue to work on all these tools as they will decrease lead times.

★ Continue to minimize work-in-process.

★ Create a multi-functional worker.

★ Once setup time goals have been achieved, create new ones.

Sustain

In Stage III, Lean Manufacturing focuses on improvement and maintenance. These are achieved by reducing variation, distributing work so that everyone works efficiently without overloads or idle time, and systematically improving standards. The steps in Stage III are to:

1. Decide on the best method for monitoring production against the pace of sales (called Leveling), using either Paced Withdrawal or Sequential Planning.
2. Refine the Pull System, especially Kanban and Quick Changeovers.
3. Implement a Visual Scheduling System using either a Control Board or Heijunka Box.
4. Implement a Runner system.
5. Focus on Total Productive Maintenance.
6. Continue to improve (Kaizen).

Total Employee Involvement and ongoing training should continue at an accelerated pace.

Leveling:
Distributing Work Efficiently

Leveling: Planning and Distributing Work Efficiently

In a plant that has achieved World Class status, the production of different parts and products are staggered over time. These plants run the smallest possible quantities and plan production daily. World Class plant managers can even change production plans with less than an hour's notice. The output of these plants corresponds hourly (and even by the minute) to the diverse mix of orders by customers. This is done to serve the customer's needs and to eliminate waste.

The efficient planning and distribution of work is called Leveling. For Leveling to occur, it is crucial that all parts, materials, tools, and information be available exactly when needed. For that reason, each station along the production line has only small stocks of parts, materials, and supplies. This includes tools and tooling. When needed, materials, supplies, and tooling are delivered. In essence, this is a "Pull" system too.

Leveling can be achieved through either Paced Withdrawal or Sequential Planning, sometimes known as Heijunka. For example, Cell A could spend all morning producing one item and all afternoon producing another item. But that may not coincide with customer demand. And it would create chronic inventories of finished goods.

Bunching production creates other problems. It produces peaks that impose a disproportionate share of production time on one process while others are idle. That is an inefficient way to manage people and equipment. But managers are always pointing out that they must bunch production and implement long runs because changeover times between jobs are much too long.

Front office processes can benefit greatly from creating a leveling system.

Leveling Time and Quantity

Paced Withdrawal: Leveling Time and Quantity

Paced Withdrawal is a system of inventory control. It refers to withdrawal of inventory on a "pitched" or small batch basis. The most important aspect of Paced Withdrawal is that the small batches are moved through the process - but always based on customer demand. For example, your Paced Withdrawal might be one box of 32 hammers every 15 minutes or one pallet of 16 toilets every 16 minutes.

Ask yourself these questions:

➡ After all is said and done, is the pack-out quantity (i.e., 32 hammers per box) OK with the customer?

➡ After multiplying the pack-out quantity over the entire day, and factoring in breaks and lunch, etc., will you meet demand?

During conversion to a Lean system, the capacity to serve your customer will change and a great deal will be learned about your customers' needs. One Piece Flow will not serve the customer, and in fact may create waste. Usually he or she will want more than one piece at a time and in a specific container of some sort. Paced Withdrawal will solve this problem.

Pack-out quantity of 14 trampolines for this customer.

Paced Withdrawal:
Leveling Time and Quantity

Paced withdrawal depends on a simple concept called Pitch. Pitch is the time frame for a predetermined unit of work to be released to the floor in order to meet takt time. Pitch is calculated by multiplying takt time by the amount of product you want to move at one time (called pack out quantity). Paced Withdrawal uses the Pitch calculation, negotiates with the customer, and arrives at a pack-out batch that will satisfy the customer's needs while Leveling your production process.

> **Pitch Formula**
>
> Pitch = Takt Time (production time for 1 unit) x Pack-Out Quantity
>
> Note: Takt time is customer-driven. Pack-Out Quantity may or may not be.

When Pitch is established, all materials and supplies can be released to the floor based on the quantity needed to produce the pitch. Some companies have used a concept called "kitting" to pre-package and store pitch quantities in a supermarket system.

In order to successfully achieve Paced Withdrawal, a company may also need assistance from suppliers with regard to delivery dates, quantities, and packaging.

An important aspect of Paced Withdrawal is the changing relationship with external customers and suppliers. Most companies have focused improvements internally. Now they will include relationships with customers and suppliers in improvements.

Pitch quantity is more than one part. But, one-piece flow should be maintained in the cell.

Heijunka: Sequential Planning

Heijunka is a sophisticated method for planning and leveling the customer demand by volume and variety over the span of a production day or shift. If there is little or no product variation, you may not need this level of sophistication. However, in plants where One-Piece Flow and a high variety of product types exist, Heijunka is a necessity. For example, an automotive assembly plant can use Heijunka to assemble two black cars, then three red cars, then two white cars, and then three black cars, all in correct sequence. All the necessary parts will flow through the process and arrive on the assembly line at the correct time.

With smaller lots or pure continuous flow, the demand for parts is subject to sudden peeks and valleys. Large orders may immediately deplete parts inventory making it difficult to manage the inventory.

Heijunka can be the key to establishing a true Lean pull system in a facility. It takes the Paced Withdrawal System, utilizing Pitch, and breaks it into units based on the volume and variety of product being produced. To do this there must be a deep understanding of customer demand and the effects of this demand on the upstream producing processes.

Heijunka is not something that can be put in place with a cosmetic Lean effort. It requires strict attention to standardization.

Sequential Planning

For example, Cell/Line A could spend all morning producing one item and all afternoon producing another item. But that may not coincide with customer demand and create chronic inventories of finished goods.

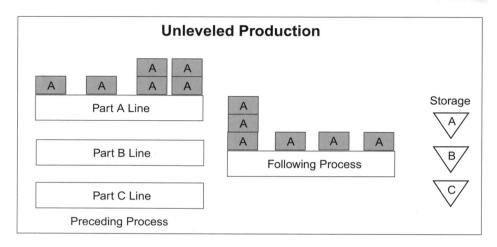

Traditional production systems concentrate work on different processes at different times.

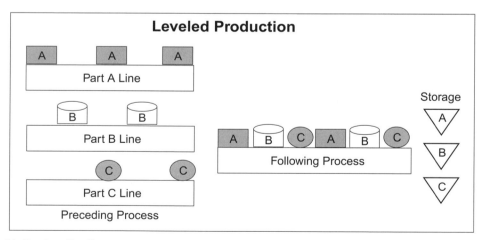

Heijunka distributes work evenly throughout the production sequence at all time

Sequential Planning

Bunching production creates other problems. It produces peaks that impose a disproportionate share of production time on one process while others are idle. And that is an inefficient way to manage people and equipment. But managers are always pointing out that they must bunch production and implement long runs because changeover time between jobs is much too long.

The solution is to distribute production smoothly and evenly throughout the day, which is the most efficient way to manage resources and time. It requires a clear understanding of customer need, excellent information and planning, and a flexible, cross-trained workforce.

Key Points for Leveling/Paced Withdrawal and Heijunka

★ If you produce a variety of products, load leveling may be the key to establishing a pull system.

★ Load leveling uses Paced Withdrawal based on pitch.

★ A heijunka box should be set up so that there will be one row for each customer (or for each color) for each product.

★ Standard work should exist for the heijunka box, Paced Withdrawal systems.

★ A heijunka box should be clearly identified as such and training conducted so all employees understand how it works.

Visual Production Control: Scheduling Made Visible

Leveling, Paced Withdrawal, and Heijunka can't work without coordination, control, and flexibility. World Class manufacturing companies have found that computerized systems are not enough. Visual Production Control is also a requirement.

Production Control Boards

Production Control Boards are a visual representation of all work distribution for an entire department or plant. Work is organized by sequence and cell (or line). Details can also be included, such as cycle time or expected parts/actual parts run. The Control Board is updated whenever there is a change so that managers, changeover personnel, quality departments, and material handlers will always have an up-to-date view of what is expected of them.

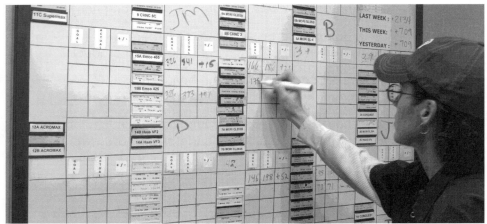

Production control boards can utilize magnetic stickers to sequence jobs for each cell. Identical stickers can be used for gauging and material handling.

Key Points to Visual Production Control

★ Involve the operators as much as practical in daily production requirements.

★ Most likely it will immediately improve productivity.

★ Solicit employees input in the design phase.

★ Utilize this tool for front office processes.

Scheduling Made Visible

Heijunka Box

The Heijunka Box, or Leveling Box, is a physical device to level production volume and variety over a specified period of time. The load is leveled with consideration for the most efficient use of people and equipment. In a Lean system this is the only place to input information on the production requirements of the day.

In a sense, the Heijunka Box is like a mailbox for production, and the runner is the mailman. Kanban cards are placed in the box in packing slip sequence at the specified pitch increment. This tells the runner exactly what to deliver, the exact quantity, where it is stored, and where to deliver it. The timing is already taken care of because the runner has a route with a specified time.

Quality audits and gauging should be made visible for scheduling.

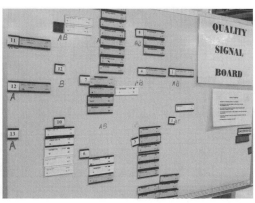

When creating a heijunka box, be creative.

Offices should create heijunka boxes or leveling wheels to distribute work loads.

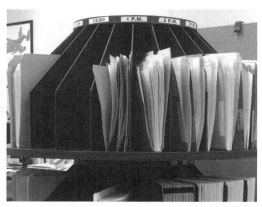

Keeping the Process Supplied

The Runner: Keeping the Process Supplied

A runner levels production by ensuring that the operators have what they need, when they need it. The runner sets the pace for the line by providing materials, supplies, information, and tooling and withdrawing product at pitch intervals.

The runner pulls materials, tooling, gauging, job kits, and supplies, and delivers them to the appropriate area. Operators should never have to search or wait.

The runner circulates between operations and covers a designated route within the pitch period, picking up kanbans, tooling, components, and finished products, and delivering them to their appropriate places.

If a Heijunka box is used, the runner removes kanbans from it to use as visual work orders. If a Heijunka box is not being used, then the runner picks up and delivers parts from store locations as required to sustain efficient flow throughout the work areas or cells. The runner continuously monitors the functioning of a line or cell. If there is a problem, the runner reports it immediately.

Key Points to the Runner

★ Ensure a priority is in place regarding the route.

★ If a pick-up of goods cannot be met, the runner should have a process defined knowing whom to contact.

★ Duties of the runner should be constantly reviewed.

Improving Equip. Effectiveness

TPM: Improving Equipment Effectiveness

Total Productive Maintenance (TPM) is the equipment aspect of Lean Manufacturing. It focuses on eliminating the wastes associated with equipment. These wastes are called the 6 Big Equipment Losses.

The 6 Big Equipment Losses

1. Equipment failure.
2. Delays due to setup and adjustments (including searching and waiting for tools, etc.).
3. Idling and minor stoppages (caused by poor operation of sensors, work blockages on chutes, etc.).
4. Reduced speed (or the difference between actual and design speeds).
5. Process defects resulting in poor use of equipment.
6. Reduced yield from startup to stable production.

The job of TPM is to:

- ➦ Eliminate equipment waste by reducing the 6 big equipment losses to zero.
- ➦ Establish ideal equipment maintenance standards.
- ➦ Maintain those standards every day.

As automation and labor-saving equipment remove certain responsibilities from people, the condition of that equipment becomes an issue because it affects output, quality, cost, delivery, health, safety, and even employee morale. In any plant, many types of equipment must be maintained. These problems are becoming more and more complex. It is difficult for plant personnel to keep up with maintenance demands.

Another issue with modern machines is that operators feel less of an ownership and are less likely to recognize or be concerned with equipment problems. The comment most often heard is that, "It's not my problem, it's a maintenance problem." In addition, maintenance personnel typically assume that if a machine is running it must be in good condition. Or, management will tell maintenance personnel to leave machines alone if they are running ("If it's not broken, don't fix it.").

Improving Equip. Effectiveness

The result is that maintenance spends most of its time on crisis manage-
ments, sporadic breakdowns, and unexpected, dramatic failures. They
are likely to ignore chronic failures - less obvious problems that contribute to gradual deterioration in machine performance and eventual
breakdowns.

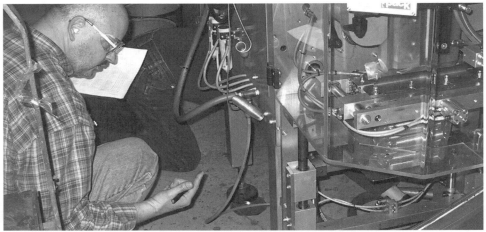

In TPM, operators perform daily checks and simple maintenance to prevent
equipment failures.

However, when workers understand their true role in production, they
can begin to change things and control the equipment. The equipment
doesn't have to control them. Even when a company shifts to completely automated production, human maintenance personnel and operators
must still maintain equipment and decide what tasks are to be performed. TPM provides a systematic method for these activities to occur.

Implementation plans for TPM vary from plant to plant depending on the
level of maintenance and specific requirements. However, five develop-
mental steps are essential for TPM implementation in any plant.

TPM Deployment Steps

1. Improve individual equipment effectiveness.
2. Implement automonous maintenance.
3. Implement planned maintenance.
4. Improve operator maintenance skills.
5. Apply early equipment maintenance.

TPM:
Improving Equip. Effectiveness

Planned Maintenance Analysis				
Target Area _____ Date _____				
Issues	Physical Appearances	Cause	Relationship to Plant, Equip., Tools	Results

Key Points to TPM

★ Implementation should be systematic and sequential.

★ Measurements should be used at all levels.

★ Deployment should be performed by cross-functional teams.

Continuous Improvement: Striving for Perfection

Continuous improvement is often considered synonoymous with kaizen (next section). Continuous improvements serve as the basis for planning, training, and deploying practices that allow the organization to attain a more efficient process.

Continuous improvement initiatives can be driven from the top of the organization or can be 'pulled' from employees who know the job the best. It is preferred that empoyees' ideas are 'pulled' from them. This can only occur if management has created the necessary support systems such as recognition, rewards, teaming and management commitment.

The Continuous Improvement System approach is more disciplined. However, when implemented as part of Lean Manufacturing, it seems natural, almost easy.

Employee surveys are an effective tool increasing employees' contributions in continuous improvement activities only if the organization has a plan to do something with the results.

Key Points to Continuous Improvement

★ Keep employees interested by giving recognition.

★ Provide necessary training for employees to learn new skills.

★ Lean is based on employees contributing their ideas.

Ongoing Events

Kaizen: Ongoing Events for the Elimination of Waste

Kaizen is a term that means "to separate out and make better." It is a method of focused training and improvement that centers on eliminating wastes of all kinds. Kaizen activities will usually form temporary teams to focus on a specific issue or problem for a short period of time (anywhere from one to five days). In that period of time, the team is given the task of creating and implementing solutions to the problem, articulating standards, and even training workers in how to use those standards.

Case Study

An example of a Kaizen event begins with the data collected in a one month period by the Quality Office in a machine shop. They were interested in wasted time for distribution of gauges and measurement tools. The total for one month for searching, waiting, and walking (traveling) was 270 minutes - 68% of the total wasted time. They concluded that they needed a Kaizen event focusing on Workplace Organization.

Quality Office September
Time Waste Study

Searching (150 min.)

Broken (100 min.)

Waiting (80 min.)

Traveling (40 min.)

Other (30 min.)

Time in Minutes

Kaizen:
Ongoing Events

The kaizen team was chosen. A two-day period was selected, with a one-day follow-up. Then the team participated in the following:

1. Training in the 5S System (Workplace Organization).
2. Analysis of data, root causes, and workplace problems concerning delivery and use of gauges and measurement tools
3. Implementation of 5S System
4. Implementation of specific problem-solving ideas
5. Standardization of improvements
6. Communication and training in new system

By the end of the second one-day event, the "wasted time" fell from the original 400 minutes per month to 70 minutes per month.

Ultimately kaizen is about ownership. It means giving employees full responsibility and authority for their jobs. People not only take responsibility to make products, they also take responsibility to improve processes, maintain equipment, and sustain a Lean environment.

Auditing results from a kaizen workshop will ensure you obtain involvement from everyone.

Key Points to Kaizen

★ Keep employees energized by rewards and recognition.

★ Management must take an active role in kaizen activities for maximum benefit.

★ When kaizen activities are completed, ensure standard work is performed.

It is important to create a kaizen form to track progress as kaizen initiatives are underway. The following is a sample form that could be utilized.

	Kaizen Report Card					

Cell Name _____ **Start Date** _____

**Value Stream
or Part Number** _____ **Close Out Date** _____

	Kaizen Goal			Kaizen Results	
Measurable	Before	After	%Improve	Actual	%Improve
Space					
WIP (pcs)					
Throughput ((ppmh)					
Set Up (mins)					
PPM					
Lead Time					

Kaizen Theme

Kaizen Team

Comments

Ask Yourself

Ask Yourself:

1. Is work leveled throughout the production area by the day, week, or hour? And how can that be improved?

2. Do workers know at what rate they should be producing?

3. Are visual controls established to identify production rate and quality needs?

4. Is there a runner system in place to ensure only value-added work is being performed by operators?

5. Is there a robust continuous improvement system in place to continually allow workers to contribute their Lean ideas?

6. Are you working with customers and suppliers in partnerships to reduce overall value stream costs?

Personal Notes

Describe the typical worker's knowledge of Lean and understanding of production leveling and visual controls:

Describe barriers in the organization that need to be overcome to be more pro-active in Lean initiatives:

List areas in which work can be more evenly balanced:

List potential team members that could contribute to the improvement of leveling work throughout the facility (do not overlook what the front offices can do to assist in this):

List action items, including who is responsible for completion:

Comments:

Summary

Summary

By gaining a basic understanding of how to level the work load through-out the facility, employees will start to understand the value of Lean. At this stage, it is important to not forget the 5S foundation and not back-track on the previous gains made.

Terms to Review

Leveling, Paced Withdrawal, Heijunka, Visual Production Control, Runner, TPM, Continuous Improvement, Kaizen

Directions

1. Review the Reality Check section, including the Personal Notes.

2. Start generating a list of ideas for activities.

3. For each activity, identify who is responsible, a start and completion date, and any additional information required (i.e., tools, training, communication, etc.).

Call to Action

Use a similar form to the sample Call to Action on the accompanying page and create a list of activities for planning and organizing Lean practices within your organization

Call to Action

Call to Action				
Target Area Boeing Panels			Date 10/31	
Lean Activity	Person Responsible	Start Date	Materials/People & Comments	Completion Date
Benchmark two companies that have visual control systems	Bud	10/31	Contact local manufacturing alliance	11/30
Meet with house-keeping committee	Terry/Beth	10/31	Keep team focused	11/15

Keys to Sustain

★ Management must take an active role in improvement initiatives.

★ Visual controls contribute to increased employee involvement.

★ Ensure front office processes are included in Lean initiatives.

★ Use people wisely and ensure they receive the necessary skills through training, benchmarking, workshops, on-the-job experiences, and other means available.

The Future of Lean

The Future of Lean

It is apparent today that continuous improvement must be a major thrust - both on an individual and organizational level. Lean (i.e., continuous improvement) must be built on the work efforts of people - contributing daily - if not hourly, to smoothing work flow and eliminating process waste and variation. The result is reducing cost in the organization. The responsibility of assuring this continues at the level required; organizations must provide the necessary support structure allowing for a Total Employee Involvement culture to emerge.

Furthermore, organizations over the past five to ten years have had good, if not great results with Lean. Many now are looking for that "next" program. Many have asked: "What is beyond Lean, what's next?" Well, the fact is, there is no "next" program or exciting word that can be used. Lean is it! It is here to stay - organizations must continually take advantage of these Lean tools and the concept of waste elimination and apply it to every part of their business. In that endeavor, organizations must look at their overall business processes and create the system structures to take Lean to *their* next level.

Toyota has stated that they have been doing Lean for nearly 60 years and are still just beginning. Lean is here to stay!

The Lean Primer

Other Books Available for the Job Shop and Small Manufacturer

BackStreet Lean - Solutions for the Job Shop - Plant Edition

The book is the how-to implement Lean of the job shop based on the best practices from world-class job shops who have shared their unique applications of Lean. Learn from those that have done it!
162 pages, 8.5" x 11", 44 photos, $55.00.

The Lean Assessment - Plant Edition

The Lean Assessment will provide a baseline upon which you can improve - and most importantly also provide a reference - depending on your score - on what areas you should focus.
52 pages, 8.5" x 11", $15.00.

The Lean Pocket Guide - Tools for the Elimination of Waste

The Lean Pocket Guide is designed as a convenient, quick reference as you learn and implement Lean manufacturing tools and techniques. Put your finger on any entry within a matter of seconds.
172 pages, 3.75" x 5.25", 120+ illustrations, $9.95.

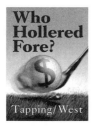

Who Hollered Fore? Lean: Controlling Your Processes By Eliminating Waste and Variation

This book is a short, easy, friendly primer on how to rally an organization in controlling processes by eliminating waste and variation.
90 pages, 5" x 7", 30 illustrations, $18.95.

The Lean Office Pocket Handbook

This guide provides the basic 13 Lean tools as applied to the administrative area. It not only explains the tools in detail, but also provides forms and worksheets for you to get started.
80 pages, 3.75" x 5.25", 70 illustrations, $8.95.

Visit **www.theleanstore.com** for more information about these books and available workshops.

The Lean Manufacturing Training Set

The Lean Manufacturing Training Set is an all-inclusive Lean training material set with the ability for customization. The Lean tools and concepts are explained in terms of actual plant examples allowing workers to better understand and apply the Lean tools. Includes: 200+ PowerPoint slides, 50+ plant photos, detailed instructions on conducting a Lean simulation, Lean Jeopardy game, (1) Facilitator Guide, (5) Particpant Guides, and (1) CD that contains everything.
200+ pages, 8.5" x 11", $195.00.

The Lean Office Pocket Guide - Tools for the Elimination of Waste in Administrative Areas

The Lean Office Pocket Guide is designed for use as a convenient, quick reference as you learn and implement Lean tools in administrative areas. Topics such as 5S, Pull, Office File System, Document Tagging, Visual Controls, Predictable Output, etc. are part of the 30+ tools being described in this book.
178 pages, 5.5" x 3.5", $9.95.

Visit **www.theleanstore.com** for more information about these books and available workshops.